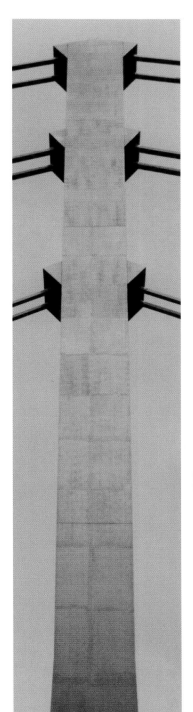

36 YEARS OF
BRIDGES

A COLLECTION OF BRIDGES

BY
MAN-CHUNG TANG

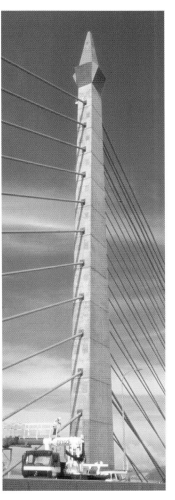

Published by TANGO INTERNATIONAL LTD., New York, USA

www.bridgetango.com

ISBN: 0-9714819-1-1

Published by TANGO International, New York, USA
www.bridgetango.com

Published in year 2002.

Printed in China

Eel River Bridge, Rio Dell, California, USA

A Few Words About This Book

Bridges are beautiful objects. Most of them are graceful and enjoyable to look at. Each bridge by itself is a piece of art, a monument. But a bridge is more than a monument. A monument really has no intrinsic value. A bridge must be functional and safe to use. In addition, it must be built within a given budget. A successfully designed bridge is a creative merge of form, function and economy.

I have been fortunate to have had opportunities to work on many beautiful bridges in the last 36 years. Thereby I have collected a large number of pictures of bridges, both in construction stages and in their completed stage. It has always been my desire to share them with those who, like me, also enjoy looking at beautiful bridges.

At the start of the new millenium, after 36 years of bridge work, and at an age of 63, I decided to make this a reality.

This book is a collection of some of the bridges I have worked on. My function in each of these structures varied - design, modified design for final construction (redesign), proof engineering (design review), construction engineering, or as a special consultant.

I hvae included only bridges that satisfy all following conditions: 1. I must have personally worked on the bridge; 2. My involvement was part of a contract, not just free advice; and 3. The pictures must be interesting, either aesthetically or from an engineering perspective.

I enjoyed every minute of work on these bridges. I hope the readers will enjoy looking at these pictures. And, for engineering-minded readers, I have also attached some brief notes about the projects.

San Francisco, 2001   *Man-Chung Tang*

INDEX OF BRIDGES

This is the list of bridges contained in this book. The numbers behind the bridge names are the page numbers. The second line describes my involvement in each bridge.

Many people contributed to the success of these bridges. I apologize for not being able to identify them here. This book is intended only as a reflection of my thirty six years of bridge work.

Mythuan Bridge, Vietnam *[131]*
Construction Engineering

Nanjing Second Yangtze River Bridge, China *[140-143]*
Special Consultant

Nanpu Bridge, Shanghai, China *[122, 124]*
Design Review and Special Consultant

Neuenkamp Bridge, Duisburg, Germany *[12-15]*
Design + Construction Engineering

Niulan River Bridge, Taiwan, China *[48]*
Modified Design + Construction Engineering

Palmetto Expressway/SR826, Florida, USA *[42-44]*
Design

Panchiao Viaduct, Panchiao, Taiwan, China *[112]*
Design

Parrotts Ferry Bridge, California, USA *[36-38]*
Modified Design + Construction Engineering

Penang Bridge, Penang, Malaysia *[52-54]*
Modified Design + Construction Engineering

Pine Valley Creek Bridge, California, USA *[6-9]*
Modified Design + Construction Engineering

Potengi Bridge, Natal, Brazil *[150]*
Design

Quincy Bridge, Illinois, USA *[121]*
Construction Engineering

Ramp I, Miami, Florida, USA *[45]*
Construction Engineering

Red River Bridge, Louisiana, USA *[106]*
Modified Design + Construction Engineering

Robert E. Lee Bridge, Virginia, USA *[17, 19]*
Design

San Francisco Oakland Bay Bridge, USA *[151-153]*
Design

Second Panama Canal Bridge, Panama *[150]*
Design

Second New Haeng Ju Bridge, Seoul, Korea *[102]*
Design + Construction Engineering

Section 9C, Central Artery, Massachussetts, USA *[44]*
Design

Seohae Grand Bridge, Assan Bay, Korea *[132-139]*
Design + Construction Engineering

Seven Miles Bridge, Florida, USA *[47]*
Construction supervision

Shubenacadie Bridge, Nova Scotia, Canada *[106]*
Construction Engineering

Sidney Lanier Bridge, Georgia, USA *[144-147]*
Design

Sixteenth Street Bridge over I465, Indiana, USA *[104]*
Design

SLRT Calgary, Canada *[96]*
Construction Engineering

South Boston Bypass, Massachusetts, USA *[98]*
Design

Sunshine Skyway Bridge, Florida, USA *[32, 33]*
Design Review + Construction Supervision

Sun Yat Sen Freeway Extension, Taiwan, China *[99]*
Construction Engineering

Tagus Suspension Bridge, Lisbon, Portugal *[108, 109]*
Construction Engineering for Strengthening

Taipo Trunk Road Bridges, Hong Kong, China *[50]*
Design

Talmadge Memorial Bridge, Georgia, USA *[66-73]*
Design

Tungling Yangtze River Bridge, Anhui, China *[55]*
Special Consultant

Twelve Mile Creek Bridge, Ontario, Canada *[100-101]*
Construction Engineering

Upper Middle Road Bridge, Ontario, Canada *[39-41]*
Design

Vail Pass Bridges, Colorado, USA *[96]*
Construction Engineering

West Seattle High Level Bridge, Washington, USA *[21]*
Design of Superstructure

West Seattle Swing Bridge, Washington, USA *[34-35]*
Design of Superstructure

Wuhan Second Yangtze River Bridge, China *[55]*
Special Consultant

Yangpu Bridge, Shanghai, China *[123-125]*
Design Review + Special Consultant

Yelcho Bridge, Chile *[10-11]*
Design + Construction Engineering

Pine Valley Creek Bridge, California

The Pine Valley Creek Bridge was the first cast-in-place concrete segmental bridge in the United States. It has a main span of 450 feet (137 m) and is 400 feet (122 m) above the valley. The area is environmentally sensitive so that disturbance to the mountain-side had to be kept to a minimum during construction.

Pine Valley Creek Bridge, California.

The challenge in building this first longspan concrete segmental bridge in the U.S. was the difficult terrain.

Working from one end towards the other end using a gantry to access directly the point of construction avoided the rugged terrain and achieved high efficiency.

As the industry was not yet prepared for this type of construction in the US back in 1972, we had to design the travelers, the gantry and the forms as well.

While the gantry rusted away in storage after completion of the project, the form travelers from the Pine Valley Creek Bridge were reused many times in the last 25 years for other cantilever bridges in the United States, Canada and overseas.

The tall piers were found to be too flexible to resist the unbalanced bending moment during construction. Therefore we installed vertical tie-downs to help resist the unbalanced moment.

All longitudinal, transverse and vertical prestressing tendons were high strength Dywidag threaded bars.

Many things were new for the US construction industry at that time. Shear tendons for large single cell box, rock anchors to nail the tall piers to the bedrock to resist uplift, even the sequence of placing concrete of the box section had to be detailed. It really was a special experience!

We actually had to design the bridge beyond the existing Codes.

There were many overseas phone conversations because Klaus Bimeslehner was working in Munich using the computer there. This was also where King-Chih Chuang learned to become a specialist on rock anchors.

The construction was very successful!

We were redesigning the bridge under the Value Engineering option at the same time the bridge was under construction. Very often we talked to Bert Bezzoni in Sacramento in the morning to agree on the design and talked to Don Ward at the site in the evening to agree on the quantities.

Now, 25 years after its completion, the Pine Valley Creek Bridge is still one of the best built segmental bridges in the United States.

Pine Valley Creek Bridge, California

Re-visiting the bridge with Juergen Plaehn twenty five years after its completion.

9

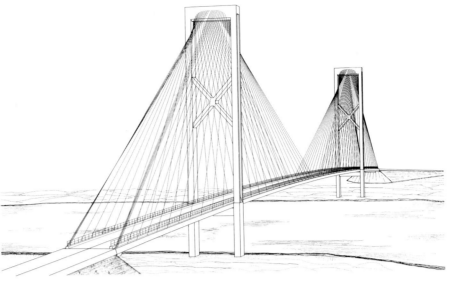

Yelcho River Bridge, Chaiten, Chile

The bridge is located in southern Chile. The main span is 150 meters. The deck is a simple solid slab with two edge girders. Both the towers and the girder are cast-in-place concrete.

How do we build an elegant and least expensive bridge in a remote but beautiful area? And, without heavy equipment!

The design of the Yelcho River Bridge is unique. Its cables, though all straight, appear to warp in space. They are anchored on a straight line transverse to the the bridge axis at the top of the towers and on a straight line parallel to the bridge axis at the edges of the deck.

Each cable consists of one single 36mm diameter Dywidag high strength threadbar tendon. The use of a single bar for every cable was made possible by varying the cable spacing along the girder so that the force in all cables is nearly equal.

The threadbar tendons came in 15 meter long pieces. They were coupled together with threaded couplers during erection to the desired cable length.

We also designed a very light and simple form traveler for the construction of the cast-in-place deck.

Yelcho River Bridge, Chile

Duisburg-Neuenkamp Bridge, Germany

In this bridge, all stays are lock-coil strand cables. They run continuously through the tower supported by saddles. Saddles were common in all early cable-stayed bridges as the concept was taken over from suspension bridges.

There are three different types of saddles: fixed, sliding and rotational. A combination of the three was often used in a single bridge to achieve the most desirable boundary conditions.

It was the first time that mechanical dampers, visible on the upper cables, were used to suppress wind-induced cable vibrations.

Duisburg-Neuenkamp Bridge over the Rhine River, Germany

At the time of its completion in 1970, the 350 meter span Neuenkamp Bridge was the longest span cable-stayed bridge in the world. It was also one of the widest. It has one single plane of cables in the middle and all side span piers are single column piers at the center line of the girder. The center spine box provides the required torsional stiffness to resist eccentric loads. The torsional moment of the girder is resisted at the tower piers and the abutments by a pair of bearings.

The side span piers are pendulum piers that allow longitudinal movement. They are hinged to the superstructure so that they can take both tension and compression.

Cables are all lock coil strands grouped together. The steel weight of the bridge, including girder, towers and cables is only 350 kg per square meter of deck area.

All splices in this bridge, including all field splices, were welded-also a first in the world.

World Records: I was fortunate to have the opportunity to work on many world record spans. But it just happened that way.

My experience is that a world record does not last very long. Both Knie Bridge (320m) and Neuenkamp Bridge (350m) were world record spans when I worked on the design and construction of them. These records were broken long time ago. Very soon, the longest span will be over 1000m.

I do not believe we should spend addition money just to get a world record. Instead we should do our best to design beautiful and technologically more advanced structures. A broken world record has no value but a beautiful and quality bridge will always be a distinguished monument of success.

Duisburg - Neuenkamp Bridge over the Rhine River, Duisburg, Germany

There was a design competition with a price bid for this project. We submitted two proposals: one 350 meter span variable-depth steel box girder and this cable-stayed girder. Our steel box girder received the first prize in the design competition and our cable-stayed girder was the first runner-up. The cable-stayed bridge alternate was significantly less expensive and was chosen for the final design and construction.

Duisburg Neuenkamp Bridge over the Rhine River, Germany

A New Steel for the Towers

The then newly developed, very high strength steel, NAXTRA70, was used for the towers of the Neuenkamp Bridge. With a yield strength of 700 MPa, the steel was so new it was not in the specifications. So I ended up developing all the design charts myself.

The towers are only 1.90 meters wide constant for the entire 49 meter height.

The performance of this steel has been excellent. The picture was taken in 2001, exactly 30 years after completion of construction.

Belle Isle Access

A Pedestrian Bridge, Richmond, Virginia

Belle Isle Access
  - Suspended from the Robert E. Lee Bridge

The community desired to have a low level access to Belle Isle, which is located in the middle of the James River. The riverside was beautifully landscaped so only an equally pleasing pedestrain path would be appropriate.

By hanging the pedestrian path from the Robert E. Lee Bridge, which was under construction at the time, the pedestrain path appears to be floating in the air, and looks exceptionally delicate.

Belle Isle Access
- suspended from the Robert E. Lee Bridge
Richmond, Virginia

The Robert E. Lee Bridge was completed in 1988. The Belle Isle Access was completed in 1990.

Belle Isle Access

Belle Isle Access
Sunset views !

West Seattle Bridge over the Duwamish River, Seattle, Washington

The West Seattle Bridge has spans of 375'-590'-375' (114m - 180m - 114m) and a deck width of 106 feet (32.3m). It was constructed in 1983 using the balanced cantilever method.

The main spans of the Acosta Bridge are designed for three lanes of highway traffic and one track of rapid transit in each direction. In the approach spans, however, the rapid transit tracks are supported by a separate structure.

Acosta Bridge over the St. Johns River
Jacksonville, Florida

The bridge was completed in 1994. The pictures were taken in 2001.

Acosta Bridge
Jacksonville, Florida

At Night,

in the Evening,

in the Morning !

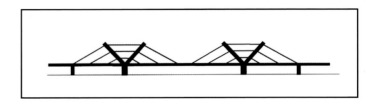

Acosta Bridge over the St. John's River, Jacksonville, Florida

The asymmetrical configuration of the bridge was a unique structural answer to the geometric restriction of the site. This also added elegance and intrigue to the structure.

In 1989, I originally envisoned a cable-stayed bridge with sloping towers, sketch left, for this bridge because the existing navigation channel at the right side span allowed only a small construction depth of the girder at that location. A cable-stayed bridge would have been a good solution to this problem. However, after careful study of the area, I believed a cable-stayed bridge would have been too imposing for the architecture of the buildings near by.

To accommodate the large main span of 640 ft. (195 m), a symmetrical bridge would have required a deeper girder depth at the side span than what was permitted. To meet the requirement of navigation clearance, the right side span was shortened to 270 ft. (82.3 m). To balance the main span, the left side span was made longer than usual, to 360 ft. (110 m), to pull more load of the bridge to the left. This resulted in an asymmetrical configuration.

*Alex Fraser Bridge
over the Fraser River,
(Annacis Island
Bridge),
Vancouver, Canada*

At the time of its completion in 1986, the Alex Fraser Bridge was the longest span cable-stayed bridge in the world. The 465 meter span bridge has a composite girder with steel longitudinal edge beams and transverse floor beams supporting precast concrete deck panels. The cables are of parallel wires within an extruded high density polyethylene pipe. The construction was completed in 30 months.

To expedite construction, we changed the construction concept from the high-lines recommended by the designer to the use of four American derricks so that it could meet the 30 month construction schedule.

Alex Fraser Bridge
over the Fraser River
Vancouver, Canada

27

Alex Fraser Bridge - Annacis Island Bridge, Concrete Alternative
Vancouver, B.C., Canada

Our concrete alternative of this bridge was a very graceful design. Unfortunately the elegantly shaped towers, even though admired by many, were too expensive for competitive bidding and therefore this alternative was not built.

During the preliminary design, Larry Bush, Ulich Finsterwalder and I had many discussions on the configuration of the girder. We started out with the two lower schemes, which were my concepts for two other bridges I was working on at that time.

We preferred a flexible girder but had concerns about aerodynamic stability because its torsional stiffness was low. At that time, not much wind tunnel test data was available for flexible girders. After many modifications, we finally ended up with the top scheme which provided higher torsional stiffness and was better aerodynamically shaped.

If I would design the same bridge today, I would use the bottom cross section.

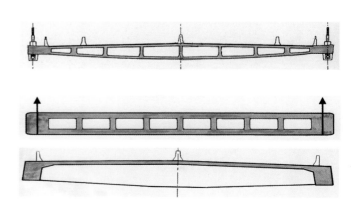

ALRT Skytrain Bridge, Vancouver, Canada

At the time of its completion in 1988, this 340 meter span was the longest for a transit bridge in the world. It carries two tracks of transit trains over the Fraser River.

Cables are of parallel wires with Hi-Am sockets. They are spaced at 11 meters apart at the deck. The deck was made of precast concrete segments, 12.56 meters wide and 5.5 meters long. The total depth of the girder is only 1.1 meters.

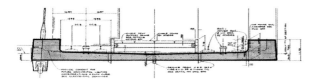

This design was done after the Alex Fraser Bridge was complete. We decided to use a much simpler section.

This was the second cable-stayed bridge I worked with E.H. Baik, who was Contractor's project manager for both bridges. When we worked together on the Penang Bridge, he sent two bright, young engineers, S.W. Kim and H.Y. Shin, to our New York office to acquaint themselves with the American way of designing bridges. After completion of the Penang Bridge in Malaysia, S.W. Kim followed E.H. Baik to Vancouver to build the ALRT Skytrain Bridge. He married a nice Korean Canadian lady in Vancouver, went back to Korea together and started his own consulting firm. H.Y. Shin got his Ph.D. in Japan and then successfully built the Youngjung Bridge near Seoul airport in Korea, the world's longest self-anchored suspension bridge to date.

ALRT - Skytrain Bridge, Vancouver, British Columbia, Canada

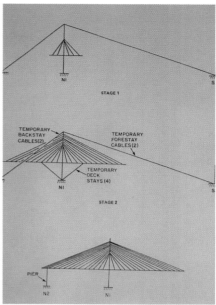

ALRT Skytrain Bridge, Vancouver, B.C.

The girder consists of only a 40 centimeter thick solid slab and two 1.1 meters deep edge beams. It is extremely flexible. A special segment lifter had to be developed for the erection of the segments.

First we cut each 11 meter long panel into two segments. The 5.5-meter long segments were lifted by a lifter, which was suspended by a large rope from the tower top so that the weight of both the lifter and the segment was not carried by the girder during the lifting operation. The load was transferred to the girder after the front cables were installed and stressed. The lifter was designed to lift two segments sequentially after each advance.

Even when the lifter was being advanced from segment to segment, it was always suspended by the rope so that most of its weight was never transferred to the girder.

To safeguard the bridge from buffeting under turbulent wind during construction, diagonal tie cables from the deck to the tower base and temporary backstay and foresrtay cables from the tower top were installed. These tie cables increased the frequencies of the bridge and thus reduced the aerodynamic responses to an acceptable level.

These temporary cables were dismantled after the end of the back span was attached to the end pier.

Sunshine Skyway Bridge across Tampa Bay, Tampa, Florida

Engineers and Fishermen:

I seldom catch a fish because I do not have the patience to sit there and wait for the fish.

During the construction of the Sunshine Skyway, we had monthly meetings of the Technical Advisory Board and the Management Board. People said that if I was in Florida, I had to take some days off and get some experience in fishing. So, one day, Tom Meredith, Jack Campo, John Sandeen and I, the four Joint Venture partners for the ocnstruction supervision of the bridge, hired two boats and went fishing. To my surprise, together, in less than one day, we racked up almost 1,500 lbs. of fishes.

I was wondering why fishing was so easy. I soon found out that the Captain had sonar and all modern equipment to locate exactly where the fishes were so our boats were always on top of a school of fishes. In addition, the Captain also set the depth of the hooks.

Poor fishes! It was not a fair match!

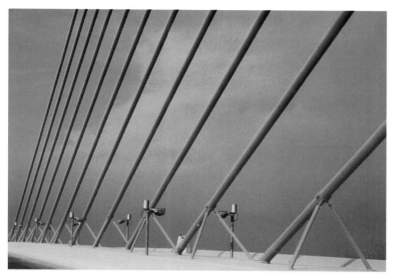

The Sunshine Skyway is a big sister of the Brotonne Bridge in France - the same concept with a strutted center spine box girder and a single plane of cables. Even the color of the stays is the same.

However, the Sunshine Skyway utilized fully precast segmental construction while the Brotonne was mixed, precast and cast-in-place.

The Sunshine Skyway Bridge was completed in 1987.

The cables of the Sunshine Skyway Bridge consist of seven wire strands encased in steel pipes. The pipes were painted yellow. The bottom picture, taken when about one quarter of the cables were painted, is quite striking.

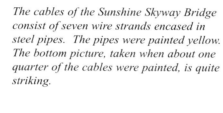

West Seattle Swing Bridge
Seattle, Washington

Erich Aigner was rather excited about a concrete swing bridge when the idea came up. So we developed various schemes: cantilever, cable-stayed, combinations........

The balanced cantilevers are most suited for the location, both technically and aesthetically. Because the high level bridge was already built, the balanced cantilever box girder is much more compatible with the high level bridge which is also a box girder.

People were rather skeptical when we recommended in 1984 building this world's longest swing bridge span of 500 feet (152.5 meters) in concrete. The bid result proved it was more economical and easier to build than the steel alternative as the bid price was about 30% lower.

The two halves of the bridge were constructed independently alongside the river. Surprisingly, or, not surprisingly, the two halves matched perfectly when they were swung towards each other.

This is a very busy waterway. The bridge was completed in 1991. It swings open almost every hour and has done so for the last ten years already.

Parrotts Ferry Bridge, Sonora, California

The bridge crosses over a lake formed by a dam. The bridge was built before the lake was filled so it could be constructed under dry conditions.

The picture at the left shows the bridge under construction by the balanced cantilever method and the picture below shows the bridge just after completion in 1979. The bottom picture was taken about 20 years after construction. The water level is now high so the lower part of the piers is no longer visible.

The area is beautiful. It is a popular place for recreation.

Parrotts Ferry Bridge, Sonora, California

The Parrotts Ferry Bridge was the first major lightweight concrete long span bridge in the world. It has a center span of 640 ft. (195 m). During construction, we were very concerned about the lack of performance data on the creep characteristics of light weight concrete. The camber was estimated based on test data supplied by the owner. The bridge did deform more than predicted but this was successfully corrected by a subsequent retroffit.

Parrotts Ferry Bridge, California - Bottoms-up !

Upper Middle Road Bridge over the Sixteen Mile Creek
Ontario, Canada

The bridge crosses over a golf course with extensive landscaping. Aesthetics was high on the agenda. It was completed in 1993.

(All pictures of Upper Middle Road Bridge courtesy of McCormick Rankin)

The bridge was built by balanced cantilever method except the end spans which used local falsework. The main span is 100 meters long.

Upper Middle Road Bridge, over the Sixteen Mile Creek, Ontario, Canada

Upper Middle Road Bridge over 16 Mile Creek
Ontario, Canada

It is always important to consider the well-being of the pedestrians in the design of a bridge. Including appropriate areas for pedestrians where they can stop, rest and enjoy the glory of nature makes the passage over the bridge a pleasant experience.

Palmetto Expressway /SR 826 & I75 Interchange
Miami, Florida

Palmetto
Expressway &
I75 Interchange,
Miami, Florida

Palmetto Expressway/SR826 & I75 Interchange

There are a total of five bridges. They were completed in 1986. This is one of the earliest precast segmental interchanges in the United States. Cranes are ideal for the erection of segments in the flat land area.

Central Artery Section 9C, Boston, Massachusetts

The Central Artery and Tunnel Project in Boston is a difficult site. The construction must squeeze between existing buildings and other structures. It is in stark contrast to the Palmetto site in Miami.

Section 9C was built using precast segments. The deck width is variable..

Piers, Piers !

Piers can have different shapes. But the piers of a bridge must blend well with the bridge superstructure and the surroundings.

The three different shapes of piers in the Acosta bridge, above, blend well with each other. The Seohae Grand Bridge, left, has tall and heavy piers. The Dames Point Approaches, middle, have clean and simple looking piers.

In Miami, the piers of Ramp I and Palmetto Expressway Interchange are elegantly configured.

I75-I595 Fort Lauderdale Interchange, Florida

There are 79 spans ranging from 36.5m to 61m, in the entire interchange, totaling 3.45 km in length with 1,366 precast segments.

Crane erection was so efficient in this project that it cut 300 days from a 1,000 day schedule. The advantage of using cranes is that many cranes can be employed at the same time. Consequently we could build several pairs of cantilevers simultaneously.

The entire interchange was built using precast segmental box girder in 1987. The relatively flat area was especially suitable for crane operations.

I75 / I595 Interchange, Fort Lauderdale, Florida

Balanced cantilever construction started at several piers at the same time. A pair of strong back steel beams was used to clamp the two cantilever ends together so the closure could be poured without concern for temperature movements, making the girder continuous.

Here, temporary steel frames at each pier were used to resist the unbalanced moment during construction.

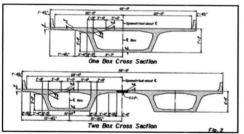

Seven Mile Bridge, Florida, USA

Here the open water was perfect for barge transportation. The segments were cast off-site and barged to the location of construction. The entire span was lifted in one piece by an overhead truss. Actually the truss was two span long so that it lifted two spans sequentially before it was launched to the next position.

Gilo Bridge, Jerusalem, Israel

At the time of its completion, it was the first precast segmental bridge, and also the largest bridge structure in Israel. A very special landscape, with a lot of olive trees!

(Picture courtesy of Public Work's Department, Israel)

Niulan River Bridge, Taiwan

A concrete segmental bridge built using cast-in-place, balanced cantilever construction.

Kipapa Stream Bridge, Oahu, Hawaii
(Opposite page)

A bridge in Paradise - a nice looking bridge in the gorgeous landscape of Hawaii!

The bridge is in Oahu, Hawaii, where the soil, when wet, will soften and lose its supporting capacity. Instead of the conventional falsework construction we introduced into this Paradise segmental concrete box girders constructed by the balanced cantilever method to build this bridge. We did this back in the mid 1970's - A state-of-the-art process.

However, here is a side story: One Friday morning, Juergen Plaehn, our manager for the Western United States, called. The Kipapa Stream Bridge in Hawaii was out for tender. We discussed and concluded that, even though it was designed for falsework construction, it was better suited for cantilever construction. The only problem was, the contractor had to have the quantity of concrete, reinforcing and prestressing steel for the tender. They needed them on Monday and we had to guarantee these quantities to within three percent. We had 72 hours to do the work.

Richard Heinen, our president said, "We should go for it!" So, we went for it!

Calling up the reserves - my wife, who happens to be a structural engineer, we designed the bridge for cantilever construction. We finalized the material quantities on time for the tender. We won the bid and completed the bridge in 1975. Surprisingly, the final quantities were within three percent.

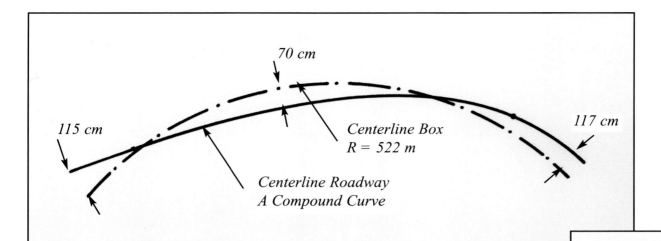

70 cm

115 cm

Centerline Box
R = 522 m

Centerline Roadway
A Compound Curve

117 cm

The total length of each superstructure is 242 meters. The typical spans are 42 meters. The single box is pre-stressed in transverse and longitudinal directions. Longitudinal prestressing consists of mainly 36mm diameter high strength Dywidag threadbars. 32 mm Dywidag threadbars were used for transverse prestressing.

The deck is 12.8 meters wide.

*Incremental
Launching*

Taipo Trunk Road Bridges
Taipo, Hong Kong, China

There were a total of eight bridges to be built by incremental launching method, a first in Hong Kong. The challenge was that one pair of the bridges was not on an uniform curve. The alignment consisted of a circular curve, a transition curve and a straight line - an alignment previously thought not buildable by an incremental method.

The very tight right-of-way would not allow any change of the alignment.

My solution was to build the center box on a circular curve, which was launch-able, while the deck retains its complex shape. As a result, the position of the deck changes continuously in relation to the box. No two cross sections of the girder are the same.

This complicated the analysis but the bridges were built successfully.

Genessee River Bridge, Rochester, New York

This bridge, completed in 1981, was the first segmental cantilever bridge built in New York State. It has two superstructures and is on a curved alignment.

Construction season in the area was short. So, the two halves of the bridge on one side of the river were built in the first season and the other two halves were built in the second season.

The 420 ft. (128m) span is still the longest concrete box girder bridge in New York..

This was one of the last cantilever bridges using Dywidag Threadbar tendons for prestressing.

(Pictures courtesy of Erdmann and Anthony)

Penang Bridge, Malaysia

Courtesy of Freyssinet-Vigouroux

Penang Bridge, Malaysia

The Penang Bridge connects the Penang island with the Malaysian peninsula. It was one of the first flexible concrete girder cable-stayed bridges in the world. The cast-in-place construction was carried out using form travelers consisting of two sections. The edge girders were cast first with one set of traveler forms. The cables were then attached to the edge girders to provide support for the deck. The slab and floor beams were cast afterwards using an after-runner form.

Each cable is comprised of 32 mm diameter high strength Dywidag threadbar tendons encased in a steel pipe. The bars were connected together from 15 meter-long pieces by specially designed couplers. The steel pipes were welded together by full penetration welds that were checked by both Ultrasonic and X-rays. Extensive fatigue tests for the bars, couplers, anchorages and welded pipes were carried out to assure the safety of the cables under cyclic loading.

I had York Kay Chan at the site to assist the contractor, Hyundai, during construction. I believe he loves Kimchi after the bridge was complete.

Communication between the head office and the site was rather strenuous because of the time lag. So when York Kay called Chung-Sing Hsieh or Cheryl Fine in New York, one of them would be half sleeping!

At the time of its completion in 1985, the Penang Bridge was the first cable-stayed bridge in Southeast Asia.

Penang Bridge, Malaysia Courtesy of Freyssinet-Vigouroux

Tungling Yangtze River Bridge, Anhui, China

Yangpu Bridge, Shanghai, China

The Yangpu Bridge in Shanghai has a main span of 602 meters. It was the world's longest span at the time of its completion in 1994. It is a part of the infrastructure to develop the Pudong area on the other side of the Huangpu River, now a booming area. It was designed and built in 29 months.

The deck is a composite structure. The edge girders are box sections and the deck consists of precast concrete panels. Cables are galvanized parallel wires encased in high density polyethylene pipe with Hi-Am type anchorages.

Second Yangtze River Bridge in Wuhan, China

The Second Yangtze Bridge in Wuhan has a main span of 400 meters. It is a major crossing in a city that is divided by two rivers into three parts.

The deck is a concrete box girder. Cables are of galvanized parallel wires encased in high density polyethylene pipe with Hi-Am type anchorages.

The contract signing ceremony for the Nanpu Bridge was well organized and elaborate. I was told that this was the first such consulting contract in China with a foreign engineering firm. - 1989.

Dames Point Bridge,
Jacksonville, Florida

Dames Point Bridge, Jacksonville, Florida

The most popular cable colors are red, white and gold (yellow). Many early German bridges have red cables. The cables of the Neuenkamp Bridge has golden color, which look very shinny in the sunlight. The Neuenkamp has few cables, so the golden color gives the cables more visibility. However, if a bridge has many closely spaced cables, the golden color is very imposing.

In most cases, white is my favorite. White cables look clean and pure.

The tower foundations are protected by large dolphins against possible ship collision.

Dames Point Bridge over the St. John's River, Jacksonville, Florida

The bridge has a 34 m wide concrete deck and a main span of 1300 feet (396 meters).
When it was completed in 1989, it was the longest cable-stayed span in the United States.
In 2001, it is still the longest span in the United States.

Dames Point Bridge over the St. John's River, Jacksonville, Florida

Dames Point Bridge, Jacksonville, Florida

Lights wake up the bridge in the night. We should always light up our bridges so that we can enjoy them all the time!

Thanks to Larry Wehner, the construction manager, who, besides managing construction, also expended tremendous effort taking all these pictures of the bridge, so that we are able to wonder at the beauty of the structure.

(All Dames Point pictures courtesy of Larry Wehner)

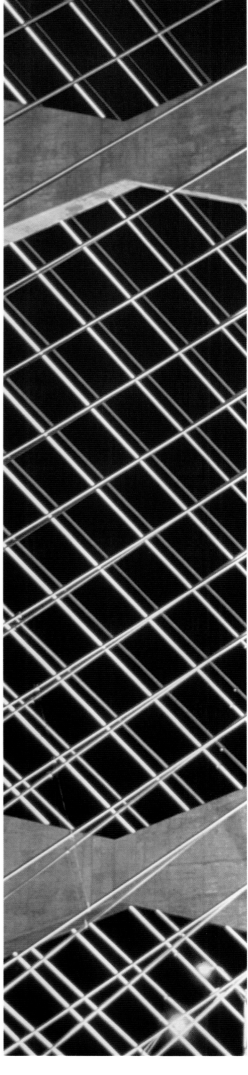

Dames Point Bridge

For the construction of this wide and flexible bridge girder, the conventional form traveler at that time would have weighed about 350 tons and would have been too heavy. So I developed the cable-supported traveler by attaching the front cable to support the front end of the traveler and was thus able to reduce its weight to 125 tons.

A satellite type connection was used to attach the front cable to the traveler. . While advancing, the traveler was suspended by a pair of C-frames.

Four travelers were used for the construction. Each traveler produced one segment in about five to six days.

The cables are 32mm diameter high strength Dywidag bar tendons encased in a steel pipe. The erection of the steel pipe was by cranes with specially designed spreader beams. The spreader beams must be able to distribute the load equally to each pick up point to avoid bending of the steel pipe.

The space inside the steel pipe was grouted with cement grout.

The towers are solid concrete columns. The cables from adjacent spans criss-cross each other inside the tower, anchoring at the opposite side of the tower columns.

Painting of the pipes was done after the grouting was completed.

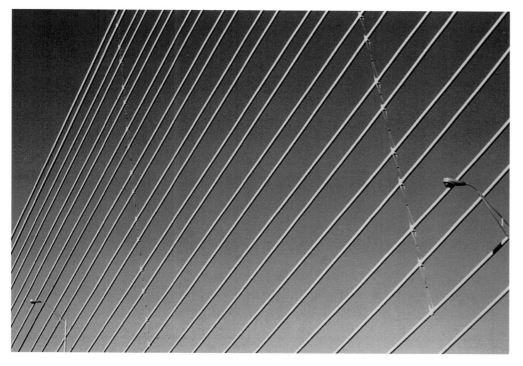

Rain-Wind Vibrations:

Some, but not all, cables vibrate with large amplitudes under the combined effect of light rain and mild, steady wind. In the mid 1980s, this phenomenon was not well understood. Nevertheless, we had to find a way to safeguard the cables.

In a meeting with Gerry Fox, Khaled Shawwaf, Herb Globig and Bob Wardlow, we decided to use tie ropes to tie several cables together so they would dampen each other. Khaled was then responsible for coming up with the "small" details.

No rain-wind vibration has ever been observed since the installation of the tie ropes.

The tie ropes are very small. They are half inch diameter galvanized wire ropes. They are practically invisible!

Dames Point Bridge - Closure Operation

When the two opposing cantilevers came close to each other, Mr. Walter Shakko started directing traffic. One of the travelers was directed to retreat and the other was advanced to finish the closeure pour - the last segment of the bridge.

The entire bridge was completed in 1989.

A hinge is located at the mid span to transfer only shear forces between the two cantilevers. The last two floor beams of each cantilever are connected at the middle by a short rib. This helps the last floor beam to resist the torsional moment from the shear locks that are located along the width of the deck.

A well designed traveler should have the capability to move in both directions. Had this capability not been included in the design of the Dames Point travelers, it would have been necessary to lower one traveler before the other traveler could advance to the closure position. This would have delayed the completion.

The approach spans of the Dames Point Bridge stretch quite a long way from each end of the cable-stayed main spans. We redesigned the piers to better support the precast concrete beams and cast-in-place concrete deck, which expedited the construction.

Southern Charm !

Talmadge Memorial Bridge, Savannah, Georgia

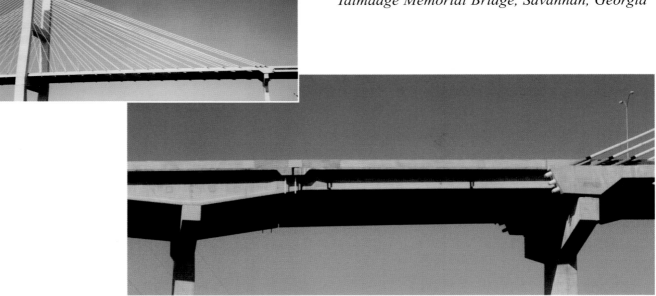

For ease of maintenance, the large expansion joint is located at the transition span so that maintenance and repair of the expansion joint will not affect the cable-stayed span.

Talmadge Memorial Bridge, Savannah, Georgia

The Talmadge Memorial Bridge has a main span of 1100 feet (335 meters) and provides a vertical navigation clearance of 185 feet (56.4 meters). Both the towers and the deck are concrete. The 24.4 meter wide deck has two 145 cm deep edge girders. The floor beams are spaced about nine meters apart. The slab is 28 cm thick, constant throughout the length of the bridge.

The bridge was completed in 1991.

Architecture: *Aesthetics is a very important part of bridge design. When I started designing the Talmadge Memorial Bridge in 1984, my very first task was to sit down with Charles Lewis, Mike Davis and Jee-Bong Louie to study the architecture of the bridge. Peter Louie would then draw up all the possible bridge configurations, especially that of the towers, based on our discussions. The shape we finally selected was very nice looking and structurally sound.*

We are happy to see that many cable-stayed bridges that were designed after the Talmadge have selected similar tower configurations also.

Talmadge Memorial Bridge, Savannah, Georgia

The cables of the Talmadge Memorial Bridge consist of 0.6 in. diameter, seven-wire strands encased in a high density polyethylene pipe. White colored PVF tape was used to wrap the surface of the black pipe. The wrapping was done with a 50% overlap.

The white color reflects the sunlight and keeps the pipe's temperature from rising too rapidly. The tape also provides good protection to the PE pipe.

White is a good color for cables. It stands out nicely against the blue sky in the background and it reflects the sunlight.

Taping of the cables

Talmadge Memorial Bridge, Savannah, Georgia

Talmadge Memorial Bridge
Savannah, Georgia, USA

Pictures taken in 2001.

Talmadge Memorial Bridge

Savannah Harbor has a very busy navigation channel. The aesthetic lighting of the bridge was designed to allow maximum visibility of the navigation lights. Therefore, its lighting scheme is concentrated on the towers. The resulting lighting presents a very unique picture of the bridge.

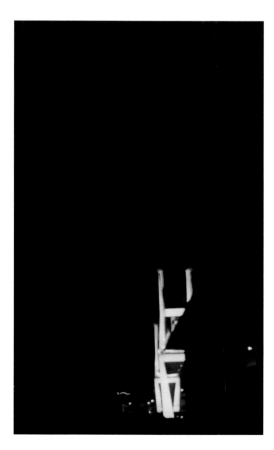

Lights, Lights !

Talmadge Memorial Bridge, Savannah, Georgia

Pictures of the bridge taken in

2001 (left), 1995 (bottom), and 1990 (right)

The 24.40 m wide girder has 1.45 m deep edge girders

Talmadge Memorial Bridge   -   Sunset over the Savannah River, Georgia

Picture by Scott Jolliff

Knie Bridge over the Rhine River, Dusseldorf, Germany

It appears that Professor Tamms, the Architect of the City of Dusseldorf in the 1960's and 1970's, liked cable-stayed bridges. Consequently, all four bridges built in the City spanning the Rhine River are cable-stayed bridges. But each has its own style and elegance.

At the time of its completion in 1969, the 320 meter span Knie Bridge was not only the longest span cable-stayed bridge in the world, it was also the longest cantilever ever built. It was almost like building the Empire State Building - horizontally!

No temporary support was allowed in the main span so the bridge had to be cantilevered from the tower to the end pier - 320 meters long.

- - - - - - - - - - - - - - - -

The bridge girder has an open cross section that consists of two edge beams and a deck plate with ribs and floor beams. Such a "plate girder" section has very little torsional stiffness. Based on my calculation the critical flutter wind speed would have been under the design flutter wind speed if the cantilever was built beyond the second cable. Consequently a temporary horizontal bracing was added at the level of the bottom flanges, making the girder into a semi-rigid box.

The bracing was dimensioned to provide the torsional stiffness required to raise the critical flutter wind speed to the design flutter wind speed. In 1965, there was no computer program available for dynamic analysis of cable-stayed bridges. I wrote my own computer program to do the tedious calculations. Our computer, supposedly one of the biggest in Germany at the time, had a memory of only 8 kb. It was not even sufficient to hold the stiffness matrix. Finally, I developed a modified transfer matrix method that significantly reduced the size of the matrices so the calculation could be fitted into the capacity of the computer.

The bridge had performed very well after its completion. These pictures were taken 31 years after construction.

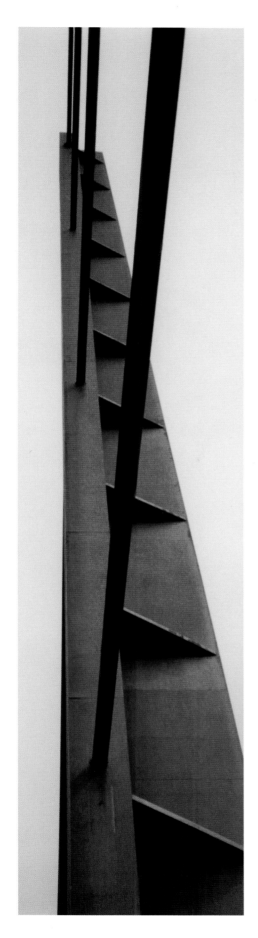

Knie Bridge over the Rhine River, Dusseldorf, Germany

The architect was very meticulous with every minute detail of the structure, down to the position of each bolt. The cable anchorages at the girder, each of which carries about 3,000 tons of load, are extremely slender. They successfully help give the bridge its delicate appearance.

The cables were lock-coil strands bundled together. They are continuous over saddles in the towers.

Knie Bridge over the Rhine River in Dusseldorf, Germany

Knie Bridge
Dusseldorf
Germany

A successful blending of
straight lines and curves

*Kishwaukee
River Bridge
Illinois*

Kishwaukee River Bridge, Illinois

The Kishwaukee River Bridge was the first precast segmental bridge erected by an overhead gantry in the United States. It was built in 1981. The gantry was very light and ran on airplane tires. Tendons were high strength Dywidag threadbars, coupled at every other segment. The erection went very fast. The maximum erection speed of seven segments a day was limited by the capability to deliver the segments to the site from the precasting yard 20 miles away.

This is one of the very few bridges with large single shear keys.

The bridge has two superstructures, 41 ft. (12.5 m) wide each. The regular spans are 250 ft. (76.2 m) long.

Eel River Bridge, Rio Dell, California

Eel River Bridge
Rio Dell, California

The bridge was completed in 1976.

Eel River Bridge - 25 years after completion

Form was attached to the cantilever during high water and winter.

The Power of Water!

The 32 mm diamter reinforcing bars were bent by water, or, more correctly, by the logs in the water.

The valley was subjected to fast floods every spring. Before the floods arrived, construction had to stop and all equipment had to be removed from the site to avoid being washed away.

We developed a spanwise construction method specifically for this project. Each span was further divided into 34 foot long segments. The falsework was one span long. The form for the 34 foot long segments was designed to slide on the platform supported by the falsework. We designed a light-weight sliding form out of wood. The form was so light that it was advanced by pulling with an electric winch that was powered by a 12 volt automobile battery as shown in the picture.

The segmental form was designed in such a way that it could be attached to the last segment of the bridge during winter and flood time so that no disassembling or re-assembling was required.

Melbourne City Link Freeway
Melbourne, Australia

For this design-build project, we designed the bridge, the casting yard, the erection gantries and provided the construction engineering and support at the site. Span length of this 13.5 km long viaduct varies from 30 meters to 50 meters. The precast segmental bridge has 3,600 segments fabricated using seven casting beds. The 47,000 square meter storage area could store 640 segments.

The segments were erected by two sets of underslung gantries in a span-by-span method.

The Down-Under was a long way from home. Paul Towell, Phil Lang, Erich Aigner and Ching Yu took turn to station at the site in Melbourne. Their function appeared to be to wake up the New York people in the night with questions.

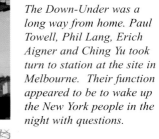

All Melbourne City Link pictures courtesy of Baulderstone Hornibrook

84

Melbourne City Link
Melbourne, Australia

Aesthetics and landscaping was very high on the agenda. The elliptical sound barrier looks very nice. The colored slanted columns are part of the landscaping. The tall towers in the far end serve no structural function. They are for decoration only.

This was a fast track project and the production had to follow ISO9000. both rather uncommon in the United States.

With Man-Pan Lee, our most organized engineer, takng care of the procedure, Park-Lun Wong, our fasttest engineer, making the calculations and Hasan El-Natur, our best business engineer, dealing with the production, this bridge became a very exciting project.

One of the most interesting discussions in this project was the one I had with Bruce Judd and Tim Ingham on how to make the barrier fail before the cantilever slab.

H3 - Windward Viaduct, Oahu, Hawaii

The viaduct is about 1.6 km long on the windward side of the mountain. Most spans are 90 to 100 meters long. The vertical webs were chosen for aesthetic reasons. With two superstructures running side by side in curves, we felt that trapezoidal boxes would not look as good.

The bridge was designed for cast-in-place construction based on the assumption that it would be difficult to find a large space for the casting yard nearby. The contractor, however, solved that problem and finally built it in precast segmental construction. By precasting the segments with a higher strength concrete, the contractor was able to reduce the webs by five centimeters.

The bridge elegantly hugs the mountain.. The view seen by motorists from the viaduct is spectacular!

*H3 - Windward Viaduct
Oahu, Hawaii*

H3-Kaneohe Interchange, Oahu, Hawaii

I believe living in Hawaii is like living in paradise!

This is one of the few construction sites where we had no problem of sending people to. As a matter of fact, when the Department of Transportation extended our contract to include the Kaneohe Interchange after completion of the Windward Viaduct, Philip Lang, our resident engineer at the site, and his crew, agreed to stay - no question asked!

Denny Creek Bridge, Washington

The bridge is about 1,103 meters long with typical 57.3 m spans located in the Cascade Mountains east of Seattle. It was opened to traffic in 1980.

The Denny Creek Bridge crosses a beautiful wooded hillside. Local citizens were very concerned about the aesthetics of the structure during the design stage of the bridge. They commissioned four groups of engineers, each to provide a different alternative for the bridge.

My answer to the aesthetics was to introduce .this slender center box girder with long wing slab. The people liked it so much that they offered a premium on this alternative so that the bid for this alternative could be $300,000 higher than other alternatives. This was something extremely rare in a government project. The bid result, however, showed that it was actually about one million dollars lower than any other alternative.

The hillside in this area is very unstable, which can pose a serious danger of rock slides if it is disturbed or shaken. Therefore no local falsework support from the ground was allowed during construction.

The foundations were hand excavated without using any explosives. After the piers were built, the superstructure had to be constructed without any intermediate support.

To meet this challenge, I developed the three stage construction method. Stage I was built spanwise in a form supported by a truss. The bath-tub shaped Stage I girder was designed to support its own weight and the weight of the formwork and fresh concrete of the Stage II deck. The Stage III wing slabs were cast using an after-runner form. In this way, the truss, which was the most expensive part of the equipment, was required to support only the Stage I girder that weighed about one third of the entire girder.

The top of the Stage I girder was 200mm below the deck surface to meet the requirement for a replaceable deck.

Patents: *I held a patent on this construction method. This was the only bridge patent I ever applied for. It was fun the first time when I got a patent, a feeling of achievement! However, I never applied for another patent since then. Personally, I believe patents inhibit development and skew competition. As bridge engineers, we are working directly, or indirectly, for the general public. It should be our goal to maximize our contributions to the society.*

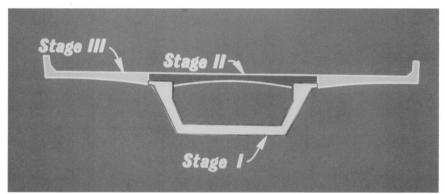

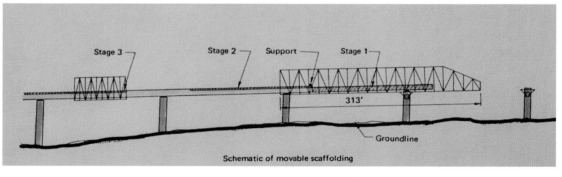

Schematic of movable scaffolding

A three-stage construction method.

Denny Creek Bridge, State of Washington

Linn Cove Viaduct, North Carolina, USA

This precast concrete segmental bridge was to be built without touching the ground - all work had to be done from the top down, including the piers, except that one temporary support was allowed at the midpoint of each of the 180 foot (55 meter) spans.

To meet this challenge, John Sutter from the Contractor and I sat in a hotel room in New York and spent most of the night exploring the various concepts of construction. Finally we decided on an American derrick. The derrick was capable of picking up the segments from the back and turning them to the front for erection. We also attached an additional boom to the crane so it could reach out to the next support point to build the foundation and pier there.

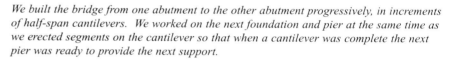

The American derrick was the lightest crane available. I sketched up the frame to support the crane on the bridge deck and had Boris Levintov finish the detail of the attachment to the box girder. This was complex because of the sharp curvatures and extensive super-elevation of the deck.

We built the bridge from one abutment to the other abutment progressively, in increments of half-span cantilevers. We worked on the next foundation and pier at the same time as we erected segments on the cantilever so that when a cantilever was complete the next pier was ready to provide the next support.

The sharp curvature and superelevation made the geometry control extremely complicated. A three dimensional analysis by Jee-Bong Louie, Joe Tse and Lionel Bellevue finally made it a success. The bridge reached the other end without any problem. It was completed in 1983.   (Pictures courtesy of Ray Stanyard)

*Chesapeake Bay
& Delaware
Canal Bridge*

92

Construction of the Chesapeake Bay and Delaware Canal Bridge started with precast span-by-span erection from both abutments. All piers were also erected in precast segments. The big overhead truss picked up the segments from its end and transported them to their final position where they were then attached to the suspenders that were extended from the overhead truss. The segments were transported lengthwise to clear the suspenders. Each segment was then rotated 90 degrees and turned back to a transverse postion before it was attached to the suspenders. However, the last two segments had to be hoisted from the ground because there was not sufficinet space to rotate the segment after the other segments were in place.

Intermediate piers were placed in the side spans of the cable-stayed bridge, making those spans the same as in the approaches. Thus, the span-by-span construction was extended to the pylons of the main bridge.

The project was completed in 1995.

Chesapeake Bay &
Delaware Canal Bridge

Glebe Island

Dames Point

Talmadge

When two cantilevers are about to meet each other at the midspan, a closure pour will connect them together to make the girder continuous.

It is a time for celebrations!

C & D Canal

Alex Fraser

Vail Pass Bridges, Vail, Colorado

These bridges in the resort area used a pigmented concrete that was pink, matching the color of the surrounding soil. Cantilever construction was selected to avoid disturbing the area. No tree cutting was allowed.

SLRT Calgary, Canada

The structure was bulit using precast segments. A pedestrian walkway is to be suspended from the box girder. It goes through the opening of the piers.

I205 Washington Approach, Vancouver, Washington

The span-by-span cast-in-place construction employed a segmental form that slid on the false-work platform, similar to the construction of the Eel River Bridge. The steel form, however, was more difficult to move.

Muskegon River Bridge, Michigan

Clean, nice looking twin bridges in a picturesque landscape - a symphony of colors !

Pictures courtesy of HNTB

*South Boston Bypass, Boston
Massachusetts*

The bridge is located in the south of the City of
Boston. It crosses over a group of busy railroad
tracks. Therefore, some piers are protected by
concrete bumpers to safeguard them from the
impact of an accidental train derailment.

This is one of the first sections completed of the
huge, 16-billion-dollar, Central Artery and
Tunnel Project. It is also one of the few composite steel girders with twin boxes.

The construction stage picture shows outrigger
supports for the cantilever slab form
hanging from the outside of the steel
boxes.

Sun Yat Sen Freeway Expansion, Taiwan, China

Elevated Roadways were added to expand the capacity of the existing Freeway.

Pictures taken in 1982

Balanced cantilevers with form travelers in cast-in-place construction

Lewiston-Clarkston Bridge over the Snake River between States of Washington and Idaho

By Chin-Ning Tang

By Chin-Chung Tang

By Yee-Yun Tang

Twelve-Mile Creek Bridge at St. Catherine, Ontario, Canada

This is one of the early precast segmental bridges in Canada. It is also one of the very few segmental bridges with ribs supporting the overhang slab.

The construciton employed a large obverhead gantry working from one abutment towards the other. The bridges were completed in 1981. The pictures were taken in 2001.

A bridge is a piece of art!

Sometimes, other artists may participate in the fun of creation too.

The precast concrete segments were erected by means of an overhaed gantry.

Joe Tse was our expert at the site to help the contractor in precasting and erecting the segments as well as other field work items. We were told that in the one year he was at the site, he ate at least 360 times at the famous MacDonalds. That should come up to only about 100 pounds of hamburgers. No wonder he did not gain weight.

First New Haeng Ju Bridge over the Han River, Seoul, Korea

The bridge is about 1.2 km long. The main spans were cable-stayed while the approach spans at both ends were built by the incremental launching method. We were called in by the contractor to perform the final design with a fast track schedule after a mishap occurred in the original construction.

The clearance limits of the railway on which the steel pieces were hauled from the factory to the site dictated the size of the box and the locations of the splices. A single box was not selected because the pieces to be transported would have to be very short to stay within the clearance limits of the railway.

A side story:

I was in Shanghai working on the Nanpu Bridge when Nils Olsson called. He said that a bridge in Korea had fallen down during construction and they wanted us to provide a new design in about three months.

I went to the site with Dennis Lee. Seeing the broken bridge in the water made us feel really sad, even though it was not our design.

A bridge structure should emanate strength and confidence, not lying broken in the water, because it is to be used by the public.

(Pictures courtesy of M.R. Huh)

The Second New Haeng Ju Bridge is located between the First New Haeng Ju Bridge and the old Haeng Ju Bridge. Its total length is about the same as the first one, 1.2 km. The center span is a concrete box girder instead of cable-stayed.

The construction of the main span was by balanced cantilever method. Both approaches were incrementally launched from the abutment towards the center span.

The picture shows the beginning of the launching operation with the steel nose installed. In the background is the First New Haeng Ju Bridge .

Second New Haeng Ju Bridge over the Han River, Seoul, Korea

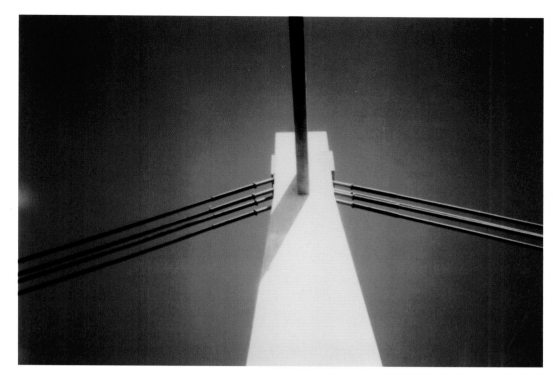

First New Haeng Ju Bridge over the Han River, Korea

Because we reuse the towers from the original construction, we had to reuse the original cable anchorage blockouts for the new cables. The new cables were Dywidag epoxy coated strand cables grouted in a PE pipe.

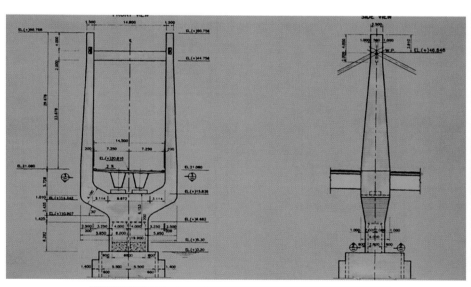

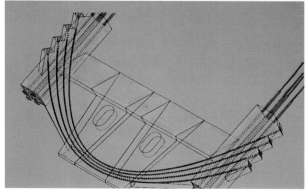

The cable-stayed main spans feature twin steel boxes and a cast-in-place concrete deck.

The cables anchor to inclined, prestressed concrete diaphragms. The cable force is transferred to the steel boxes by a combination of headed, round shear studs and welded shear lugs.

The concrete deck is transversely and longitudinally posttensioned.

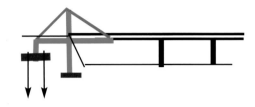

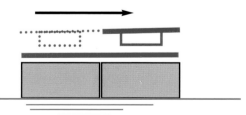

16th Street Bridge over I465, Indiana

A cable-stayed support was created so that a pier could be removed to allow the widening of the roadway. The tower was located at the abutment. The back staying cables were anchored to an anchor pier which was tied down with rock anchors. The cable-stay system was completed before removing the pier so that the construction did not interfere with traffic.

The construction was completed in 1975. (Picture courtesy of Maurice Miller)

Inter-City Bridge, Trenton, Ontario, Canada

There were two requirements for the construction of this bridge replacement: traffic could not be stopped and it had to be on the same alignment.

So, the new bridge was built next to the old bridge. Traffic was diverted to the new bridge while the old bridge was being dismantled. The new bridge was then pushed laterally onto the old bridge alignment in one night.

(Picture courtesy of Vic Anderson, Delcan)

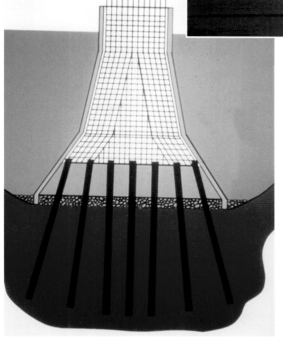

Deep Water Piers of the I-205 Columbia River Bridge Portland, Oregon

To build the deep water piers, a large dumbbell shaped steel form was used.

The piles were driven first. The dumbbell was floated to the location and sunk over the piles. A seal concrete was then poured. Water was pumped out of the dumbbell and people were able to work inside the dumbbell under dry conditions. After placement of reinforcing, the dumbbell was filled with concrete. It was then lifted by hydraulic jacks after the concrete had reached the pre-determined strength.

One dumbbell form was used to construct all deep water piers of this bridge.

The superstructure was built by the balanced cantilever method with precast and cast-in-place segments in 1981.

Red River Bridge, Louisiana

Double wall pier provides more space for the starter segment in cantilever construction. It can also better accommodate longitudinal movement due to temperature, creep and shrinkage. However, it is usually aesthetically not as pleasing.

The bridge was completed in 1984.

Shubenacadie Bridge, Nova Scotia, Canada

Its 700 ft. (213.4m) main span has been the longest span concrete box girder bridge in Canada since its completion in 1978.

Dywidag high strength threadbar tendons were used for the longitudinal, transverse and vertical posttensioning.

Construction progressed very well and often achieved three-day cycles for each segment.

The Humen Bridge crosses the Pearl River at the historic Fort of Humen. It was one of the first major suspension bridges in China. Its 888 m main span was the country's longest span at the time of its completion in 1997. The girder is a steel box. The cables are made up of prefabricated parallel wire strands. (Pictures courtesy of HPDI)

Tagus River Bridge, Lisbon, Portugal

Spinning the second cable above the original cable.

The geometry of the first cable is relatively simple. The geometry of the second cable, however, is much more complicated because it has to match the first one while the loading on the cable thruogh the additional hangers is rather indeterminate. Paul Towell and Nick Morris were in constant contact with Ron Crocket at the site to make sure everything came out perfectly. It did!

Tagus River Bridge, Lisbon, Portugal

The bottom deck of the suspension bridge was to be strengthened to carry heavy rail. All bracing members and numerous chord members had to be replaced or strengthened to meet the increased demand. In order to carry out this replacement work without interrupting traffic, we developed a moving platform that was clamped to the truss. The platform was designed to temporarily become part of the truss to allow transfer of the loads in the truss so that members of the bridge could be removed and replaced.

The replacement of the weaker members in the truss was done before the second pair of cables was installed. The additional weight caused a very noticeable sag of the stiffening truss of over three meters at the midspan. However, this was as predicted and the stresses were all within the allowable limits.

The shape of the bridge returned to normal after the second cable was installed and the new hangers picked up the additional load.

(Pictures courtesy of DSD, Germany)

Burlington Skyway, Burlington, Ontario, Canada

An interesting contrast of new and old!

Two bridges, side-by-side, each represents the state-of-the-art of its time.

The new bridge, constructed in 1985, not only stands in good contrast to the old bridge, but contrasts against itself. It has a concrete main span and steel composite approach spans - a combination representing the most efficient form of structure at the time.

Small but Simple !

Bedford Bypasses No.1 and 2, Nova Scotia, Canada

Solid concrete spine girders can be very efficient for construction of small to medium span bridges. The form work is simple and at the bottom. All work can be done from the top, making it easy to place reinforcing and concrete.

After these bridges were completed in 1979 in Nova Scotia, several similar structures were built in Calgary and Edmonton, Canada.

Kao Ping Creek Bridge, Taiwan, China

The 300 m span bridge is the longest span in Taiwan at the time of its completion. It has a concrete box girder in the back span and a steel box girder in the main span. The deck is close to the ground so that the girder was supported on falsework during construction.

(Courtesy of Chi Po Lin)

Panchiao Viaduct, Panchiao, Taiwan, China

- A one and a half kilometer long twin structure in the heart of the City of Panchiao near Taipei. Underslung trusses were used to erect the segments in a span-by-span construction. It was completed in 1993 and was one of the first precast segmental bridges constructed in Taiwan.

Bob Patterson went to the site to help the contractor in the precasting and erection. The job went very well and Bob developed a taste of Chinese food. After a year, his handling of chopsticks was as good as his handling of precast segments.

Dong Dai Road Viaduct Shinchu, Taiwan, China

- A 1.6 km long viaduct constructed in precast concrete segments and erected in balanced cantilevers. Cranes were used to erect the segments.

The bridge was completed in 1996.

At the time of its completion in 1976, this 790 ft. (241 meters) span bridge was the world's longest concrete girder bridge. It was located in the South Pacific, connecting the islands of Koror and Babelthuap. The original design had a shorter main span which had both piers located in

the water. To avoid building the piers in the swift water, the Contractor proposed, and the owner agreed, to extend the center span and located the piers on land.

We fixed the superstructure to the piers so as to eliminate any maintenance problem with bearings. We also placed a sliding hinge at the midspan to accommodate relative axial movement of the two cantilevers due to creep, shrinkage and temperature changes.

The construction was very successful except that the concrete creeped excessively, probably due to the local aggregate. Significant creep was still detectable even 15 years after construction. As a consequence, the bridge showed excessive deflection, especially noticeable at the hinge location.

Even though investigations showed that the safety of the bridge was never in doubt, rehabilitation was carried out in 1996 to improve the sagging appearance. The rehabilitation scheme called for jacking the cantilevers apart at the hinge, connecting the cantilevers monolithically and adding large amount of longitudinal posttensioning. Two months after the rehabilitation was completed, the bridge collapsed into the water.

Based on my personal observation, the failure was initiated by buckling of the top slab. With many layers of prestressing tendon ducks embedded in it, the deck slab behaved more like multilayers of thin plates that would buckle under rather small compression. The deck was not capable of resisting the very high compressive forces added by the rehabilitation. As a matter of fact, the failed deck did show typical pattern of plate buckling.

The time lag between application of high compression and the actual failure was quite typical in concrete strutures where cracking and effect of creep took time to propagate.

Damages in other parts of the bridge would also support such a failure mechanism.

The tower foundation was complete before the design of the superstructure. It was not capable of resisting the unbalanced bending moment during construction. Hence, front and back tie cables were used to stabilize the tower during construction stages.

The ties were simple seven wire strands grouped together in a bundle and anchored to a footing supported by piles and ground anchors.

One day when we were young !

East Huntington Bridge over the Ohio River, West Virginia

The segments were precast in a yard nearby using a long line method and then were barged to the site. The floor beams were steel wide flange sections to reduce weight. It was the first longspan bridge that used an 8,000 psi concrete.

The cables in this 900 ft. (274 m) span cable-stayed bridge are parallel wires grouted within a high density PE pipe with cement grout. Cable anchorages are of Hi-Am type with epoxy zinc powder and steel balls.

Courtesy of Melbourne Brothers Construction Co.

East Huntington Bridge
over the Ohio River at Huntington,
between West Virginia and Ohio

The contractor had a big crane so we tried to make use of it instead of fabricating new lifting equipment to erect the precast segments. Back in 1982, however, use of a floating ringer crane to erect the 275 ton segments was rather novel.

The erection scheme had to be designed for a 12 inch vertical motion of the floating crane caused by the wave action in the river. We developed a steel hinge mechanism between the new and the previous placed segment to accommodate this vertical motion of the floating crane.

The bridge was completed in 1985.

Baytown LaPorte Bridge, Houston, Texas

The Baytown LaPorte Bridge was completed in 1994. Its main span is 1,250 ft. (381 m) long. It has two separate composite deck girders each of which is 78 ft. (23.8 m) wide and carries three lanes of highway traffic.

At the time of its completion in 1995, the Baytown Bridge was the cable-stayed bridge with the largest deck area in the world. The twin deck was selected so that if one deck was closed because of a traffic accident, the other deck could remain open to traffic.

(Pictures courtesy of URS-Greiner)

Baytown LaPorte Bridge over the Houston Ship Channel
Houston, Texas

Baytown LaPorte Bridge over the Houston Ship Channel, Texas, USA

Four American derricks were employed for the erection. The construction was by the typical cantilever method. For each segment, the steel frame, each consisting of two floor beams and two edge girders, was hoisted into place by the derrick. The precast deck panels were also placed by the derrick.

Diagonal and vertical tie downs were used to stablize the structure during construction against turbulent wind. The vertical cables were held down by tension piles.

Baytown LaPorte Bridge, Houston, Texas

The Quincy Bridge has a main span of 900 feet (274 meters) with concrete towers and a composite deck. This is the only composite bridge in United States that has both longitudinal and transverse prestressing throughout the length of the bridge. The connection between the steel girder and the concrete deck is provided by shear studs welded to the steel girder inside rectangular openings in the precast panels. Cables are Dywidag epoxy coated seven wire strands with bonded sockets grouted in a high density PE pipe. Erection was carried out using two American derricks.

The bridge was completed in 1987.

Quincy Bridge over the Mississippi River, Illinois - on the opening day

Nanpu Bridge, Shanghai, China

Napu Bridge
Shanghai,
China (left)

The citizens of
Shanghai had
dreamed of a
bridge crossing the
Huangpu River,
connecting the two
parts of the city, for
over a century.
Finally, in 1991,
they got their wish.
The Nanpu Bridge
is an important link
on the ring road of
the City and plays a
significant role in
the development of
Pudong, the area
on the other side of
the river.

Yangpu Bridge
Shanghai
China (right)

The Yangpu Bridge
is located north of
the Nanpu Bridge.
Completed in 1994,
it is the other cross-
ing over the
Huangpu River on
the ring road of the
City.

124   *A Tower Leg of the Nanpu Bridge, Shanghai, China*

*Yangpu
Bridge,
Shanghai,
China*

Glebe Island Bridge, Sydney, Australia

Glebe Island Bridge, Sydney, Australia

The Glebe Island Bridge was opened to traffic in 1997. It was built to accommodate the heavy traffic expected during the 2000 Olympics.

The girder is continuous over five spans. The main span is 345 meters. The deck is 32 meters wide. Both the towers and the girder are of concrete.

Cables are Freyssinet type seven-wire strands, coated with wax, and individually sheathed. The strands are enclosed in a PE pipe without grout.

(Pictures courtesy of Baulderstone Hornibrook)

Form traveler of the Glebe Island Bridge, Sydney, Australia

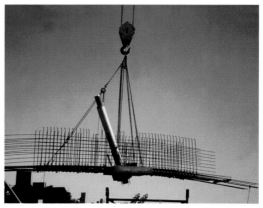

Precast Cable Anchorage Block

Form Traveler for the Glebe Island Bridge

The one most important piece of equipment in the construction of a cast-in-place cable-stayed bridge is the form traveler, the design of which basically determines the speed and ease of construction. A form traveler must be stiff, strong, light weight and easy to operate.

The Glebe Island traveler is a further development of the Dames Point traveler. This concept has been used by almost all flexible girder cable-stayed bridges world wide.

The design must also be simple and robust, such as the cable attachment satellite shown in the right. It is a simple combination of welded steel pipes and plates. I have always tried to avoid custom made steel casting and high precision parts so that, if necessary, they can be easily replaced locally

The satellite is the connection point of the front cable to the traveler. It is more complicated in the Glebe Island Bridge because the cable is inclining in both directions.

Courtesy of Freyssinet

Attaching cable to the satellite

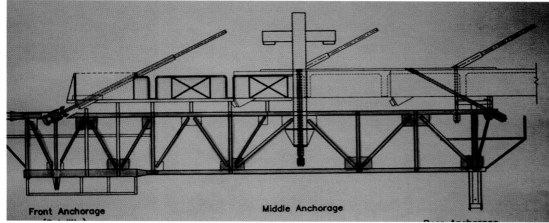

Front Anchorage **Middle Anchorage**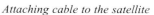

Position for concrete pour

Position for advancing traveler

C–Hanger Frame **Guide Channel**

Satellite

Rear Support

129

Glebe Island Bridge

The bridge definitely made navigation across the City much more pleasant for the participants and visitors of the 2000 Olympics.

Construction of the bridge with only one form traveler is a first. The rolling frames used for the end spans were an efficient application. The frames supported the formwork during concrete pours. They also served as tie downs under turbulent wind to reduce the buffeting responses.

The bridge was built in two halves. After the first half was complete, the traveler was lowered onto a barge and moved to the other side of the bay for the construction of the second half of the bridge. The rolling frames were moved in a similar manner.

Due to the flexibility of the edge girders, a spreader beam was added to the C-frame to distribute the traveler load for more support from the deck. This eliminated the cable adjustments which might have been required during advancement of the traveler.

A Story: The media is usually very quick to report problems, and, sometimes, non-problems as well! Hugh Bishop used to tell the story that at the time the site was preparing to make the closure pour, the traveler was only on one of the cantilevers so that the end of this cantilever deflected about 60 cm more than the opposite cantilever end because the other end had no traveler. The media was too quick to suggest that the construction had made a big mistake and the bridge, after completion, would have a big bump at the midspan. Actually the final shape of the bridge girder is excellent!

My Thuan Bridge, Vietnam

The My Thuan Bridge is the first cable-stayed bridge in Vietnam and the second crossing over the Mekong River. The bridge carries four lanes of traffic and provides a vital link on National Highway No.1. It was opened to traffic in May 2000.

The main cable-stayed structure over the river has a 350 m central span and two 150 m side spans.

The 23.66m wide in-situ concrete superstructure is supported by 64 stay cables. The deck slab is carried by two 2.0m deep longitudinal edge beams

This cable-stayed bridge has all cable anchorage blocks located outside of the longitudinal edge beams. We precast these anchorage blocks up to about mid-height of the slab. The stay cables were anchored to the anchorage blocks and stressed before casting the segment. These precast anchorage blocks were stressed down to the upper chords of the traveler so the vertical component of the cable force was taken to the traveler directly. The longitudinal component of the cable force was resisted by a strut from the new anchorage block to the previously placed anchorage block. This eliminated the satellite in our traveler design.

The vertical wind tie-downs were anchored to a platform supported by piles. We added dead weight to the platform to activate the compression capacity of the piles.

The Freyssinet cables consist of individually waxed and sheathed seven-wire strands. Each cable has a polyethylene outer pipe for protection.

I asked Hugh Bishop and J.R. Tao on how much Vietnamese our people had learned. Well, everyone now knows how to <u>write</u> a few words in both Vietnamese and English, "1,2,3,4, 5, ..."

Seohae Grand Bridge at Assan Bay, on the West Coast of Korea

The 470 meter span cable-stayed bridge is located at Assan Bay in the west coast of Korea. It was the longest bridge span in Korea when it was completed in the year 2000. It features two concrete towers and a composite girder. The deck is 34 meters wide. It has two steel edge girders. The steel floor beams are spaced at 4.10 meters center to center. A longitudinal stringer runs along the bridge centerline to provide better support for the precast deck panels during construciton. These concrete panels are 31 cm thick near the tower and changed to an inverted bathtub shape when the axial compression in the girder gradually reduces.

The structure, located at the entrance of the harbor, will symbolize the Gateway to Korea.

(Picture courtesy of Daelim Industrial Company)

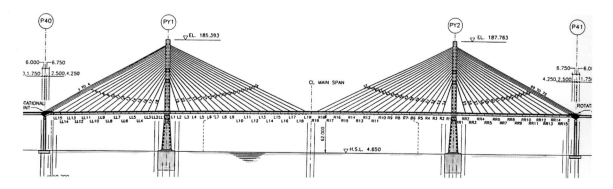

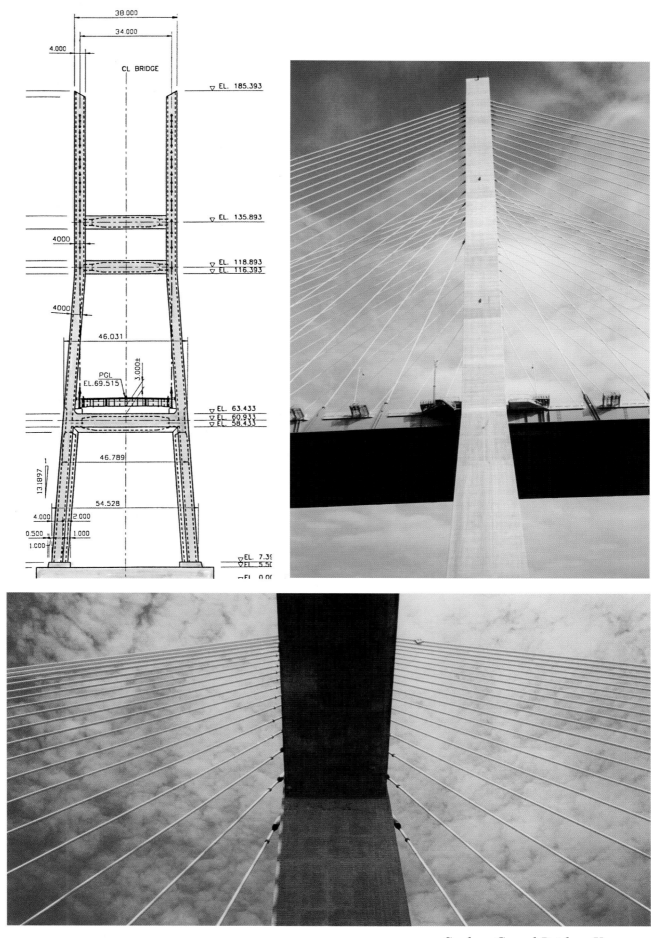

38.000

34.000

4.000

CL BRIDGE

▽ EL. 185.393

▽ EL. 135.893

4000

▽ EL. 118.893
▽ EL. 116.393

4000

46.031

PGL
EL.69.515

3.000±

▽ EL. 63.433
▽ EL. 60.933
▽ EL. 58.433

46.789

13.1897

54.528

4.000   2.000

0.500   1.000

1.000

▽ EL. 7.39
▽ EL. 5.50

EL. 0.0

Seohae Grand Bridge, Korea

133

Seohae Grand Bridge, Korea

*Seohae Grand
Bridge, Korea*

Seohae Grand Bridge, Korea

The pier segments of the girder were assembled on the ground and lifted into place using a large floating crane. Each of the 1,700 ton segments was lifted in one piece.

Placement of the end segment of the girder

Gloria Huang worked on this project. She went with me to Korea several times to attend project meetings. Lady engineer was still rather rare in Korea at that time and she was very well treated by our Korean friends.

Gloria claimed to be able to eat anything on the table: Kalbi, Kimchi, Ginseng Chicken. However, when a cut-up octopus, with its legs still moving, was served, she gave up!

Another engineer of ours, Dennis Jang, is a Buddhist. Luckily, he was not there when the octopus was served.

An inverted kingpost was used to jack up the floor beams before casting the gaps of the slab panels to introduce a compression stress into the deck slab.

Lifting of the steel frame - edge girders and floor beams

Seohae Grand Bridge, Korea

Obviously technology, especially with respect to communication, has progressed significantly from the time we built the Penang Bridge in the early 1980's. Thanks to e-mail and fax machines, Kook-Joon Ahn and Erich Aigner, our engineers at the site, no longer needed to call the office in the middle of the night. Dennis Jang and Mark Chen, sitting in San Francisco, just read the mails every morning and could answer all the questions before they woke up from sleep in Korea Digital pictures from the site also made us feel more intimate with the progress of the project.

Seohae Grand Bridge

The bridge uses Freyssinet cable system. Each cable consists of a bundle of galvanized seven-wire strands, individually waxed and sheathed . The external PE pipe has a helical rib to suppress rain-wind vibrations.

The cable anchors at the deck level are bolted to the edge girder webs. This eliminates the danger of fatigue cracking under cyclic loads. Its direct attachment to the web plate also minimizes the eccentricity of the anchorage.

Putting the cable anchorages above the deck offers easy access for maintenance inspections.

Nanjing Second Yangtze River Bridge, Nanjing, China

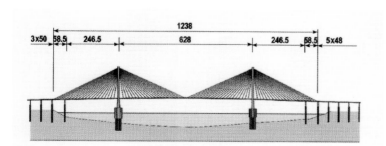

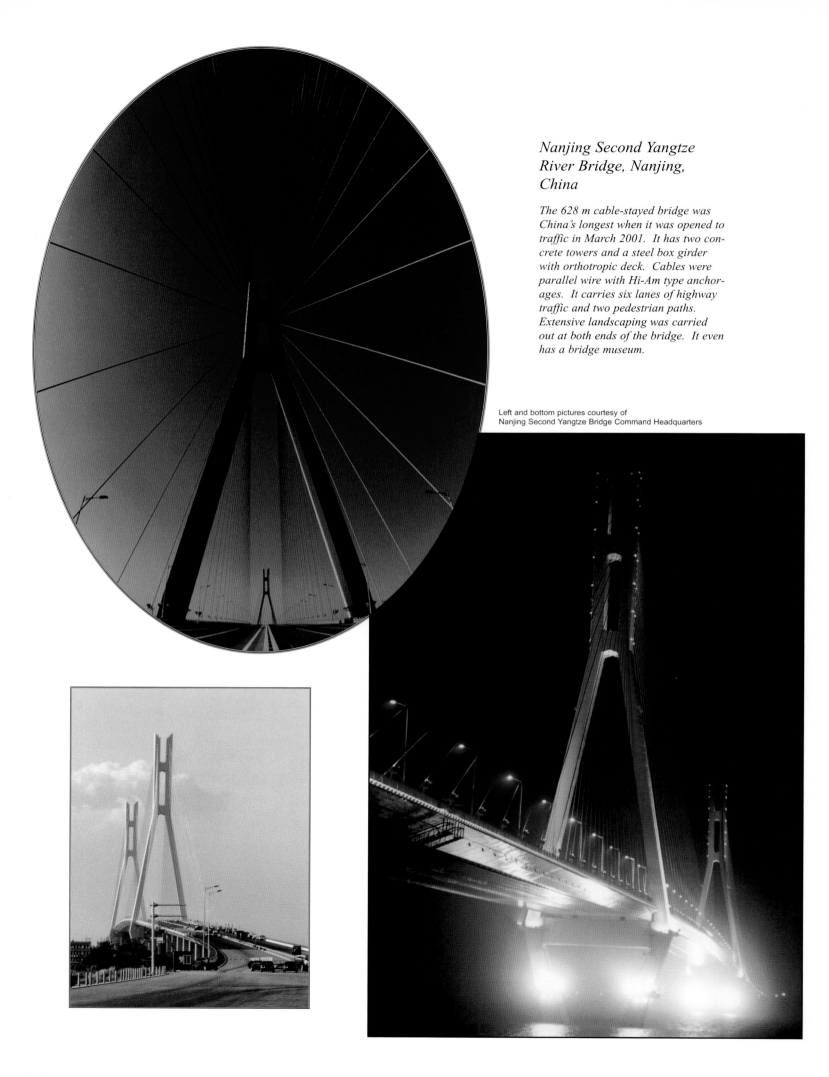

Nanjing Second Yangtze River Bridge, Nanjing, China

The 628 m cable-stayed bridge was China's longest when it was opened to traffic in March 2001. It has two concrete towers and a steel box girder with orthotropic deck. Cables were parallel wire with Hi-Am type anchorages. It carries six lanes of highway traffic and two pedestrian paths. Extensive landscaping was carried out at both ends of the bridge. It even has a bridge museum.

Left and bottom pictures courtesy of
Nanjing Second Yangtze Bridge Command Headquarters

Nanjing Second Yangtze River Bridge

The cables are galvanized parallel wire strands with extruded PE cover. To eliminate rain-wind vibrations the cables are wrapped with a spiral wire on the surface. In addition, a damper is installed at the lower end of each cable. These measures effectively dampen all cable vibrations.

*Sidney Lanier Bridge,
Brunswick, Georgia, USA*

*Bridge is scheduled for completion
in 2002.*

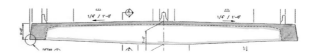

Sidney Lanier Bridge, Brunswick, Georgia

One pair of form travelers are used for the construction. Therefore, one half of the bridge is completed first. The form travelers are then moved to the other tower to build the second pair of cantilevers.

The towers are protected by sand islands against possible ship impact.

The existing bridge, with a lift span, will be demolished after the new bridge is opened to traffic.

The old lift bridge, visible behind the new bridge, provides a clearance of only 250 feet (76.2 m), is far too narrow for safe navigation of many large ships, the width of which may be close to 200 feet (61 m). It was hit and damaged several times by ships in the last decade.

*Sidney Lanier Bridge, Brunswick
Georgia*

Sidney Lanier Bridge, Brunswick, Georgia

This is a sister structure of the Talmadge Memorial Bridge. The population in the area liked the Talmadge Memorial Bridge so much that they requested to have a similar structure in this location. It has the same configuration as the Talmadge Memorial Bridge except it's main span is 1,250 ft. (381 m), a little longer and the cable arrangement is symmetrical to the tower. The towers are in the water and are protected against possible ship collision by sand islands around the footing.

The vertical clearance is also 185 feet (56.4 m).

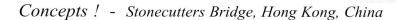

Concepts ! - Stonecutters Bridge, Hong Kong, China

The bridge is located at the harbor entrance so the configuration of ship masts should complement well with the environment. The splitting cables would offer a very special feeling to the passengers.

Outriggers and vertical tie cables stabilize the single pole tower. Consequently, the mast can be made very slender. They are designed to withstand the highest possible wind in Hong Kong.

Beauty is in the eyes of the beholders!

Every time we participate in a competition, the first question is always the taste and the preference of the selection panel members. Unfortunately this is usually unknown. We just propose the one we like best.

Sitting in a room with Kevin Hart, the Architect, we went through many possible schemes: conservative ones, ultra futuristic ones, and some, we might call, cool ones. Finally we decided on these two rather progressive schemes for this world's longest cable-stayed span.

It received the third prize!

Second Crossing over the Panama Canal, Panama

A preliminary rendering of the 420 m span bridge. The design must consider minimizing interference with the busy navigation channel during construction.

Work in progress !

Potengi Bridge, Natal, Brazil

A beautiful bridge for a beautiful resort. A restaurant is attached to the tower. Monorail suspended from the underside of the bridge will carry people to and from the restaurant.

Tamshui Bridge, Taiwan

The one kilometer long bridge features restaurants, viewing platforms, and other tourist attractions. The bridge girder is hollow and is designed for a shopping mall.

Concepts !
Concepts !

Cable-Stayed Alternatives, San Francisco Oakland Bay Bridge, California

Both cable-stayed bridges and self-anchored suspension bridges were studied.   These were cable-stayed alternatives .   The self-anchored suspension bridge (next page) was selected for the final design.

San Francisco Oakland Bay Bridge - Eastern Spans
San Francisco/Oakland, California, USA

The selected concept for the main span - a self-anchored suspension bridge.

The new eastern spans of the San Francisco Oakland Bay Bridge is a seismic safety replacement project. It is to replace the old eastern spans which were found to be vulnerable to a major earthquake in the Bay Area. The 3.6 km long bridge has a dual box girder, each of which carries five lanes of highway trafic plus shoulders. Each box girder is designed to carry a light rail system. A 4.8 m-wide pedestri-an/bike path will be attached to the east-bound structure.

The new bridge is designed to be operable almost immediately after a major earthquake in the area.

The bridge consists of a 385 m span self-anchored suspension bridge, a 2.4 km long concrete segmental bridge, called "skyway", a transition structure from the Yerba Buena Island Tunnel to the main bridge and an approach structure where it touches down in Oakland. The first section of this project was tendered in December 2001.

The self-anchored suspension bridge will be the largest in the world when it is completed. It has twin steel boxes with orthotropic deck. The twin boxes are connected by transverse cross beams. The tower is 160 m tall, the same height as the suspension bridge towers in the western spans. The single tower actually consists of four columns connected together by shear links. The shear links will yield in shear during a major earthquake, thereby absorb large amount of energy so the columns will remain elastic. The shear links are attached to the columns by high strength bolts. They can be replaced easily. The main cable is 75 cm in diameter, anchored at the eastern end of the bridge. It loops around the west end of the bridge over three saddles.

The 160 m span skyway has two single concrete boxes with no connection between them. The footings are supported by large, concrete filled steel pipe piles, about 100 m long each.

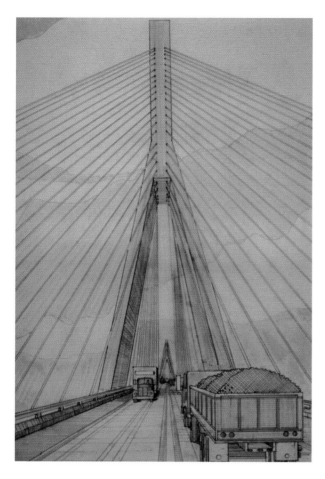

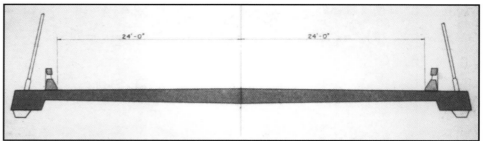

Portsmouth Bridge over the Ohio River

In 1983, I proposed this solid slab deck for the Portsmouth Bridge over the Ohio River with a main span of about 300 meters. The slab was 60 cm thick at the center and tapered to 38 cm at the face of the 84 cm deep edge girders. The slab was designed as a flat plate with post-tensioning running in both directions. Unfortunately, this design was not built.

Concepts! Concepts! Concepts!

Conceptualization is the most creative and imaginative process in the design of a bridge.

Here is a collection of interesting concepts developed for various bridges.

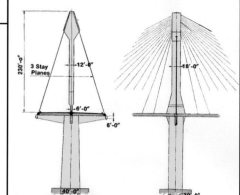

Baytown Bridge, Texas, 1988

Single leg tower with three planes of cables supporting a flexible deck. The slender tower is braced transversely by cables attached to outriggers at the towr location.

Woodrow Wilson Bridge, Washington D.C.

The almost transparent arches in white concrete would have made a spectacular monument. Its main arch was large enough to allow passage of local vessels. However, a bascule span with lower level approaches were selected for the final design.

Mathews Bridge Extension, Jacksonville, Florida, 1993

The goal was to add more lanes to the existing structure at a minimum cost. The foundations were close to their capacities so not much structural dead load could be added. At a brainstorming session with Hanskarl Bandel and Teddy Theryo, I started with an arch because it was the lightest structure, and Hanskarl moved the arch around and put it on top of the truss. We then placed the tension tie of the arch along the upper chord of the truss to give the arch a very clean and simple appearance.

Williamsburger Bridge, 1988

The bridge is inside New York City where there are many tall buildings. A bridge like that would have been quite harmonious with the surroundings. The two towers would house a museum, a public viewing platform, resturants and the administrative offices. It was designed to be built with minimum interruption of traffic on the existing structure.

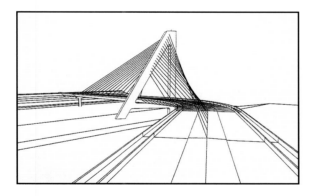

Natoma, 1993

Guaratuba Bridge, Brazil, 1989

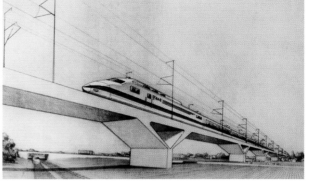

1992

1994

Concepts !
Concepts !

1991

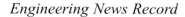

Engineering News Record

In 1999, in conjunction with its 125 year anniversary celebration, the editors of Engineering News Record identified Dr. Man-Chung Tang as one of the world's 125 top people of the past 125 years for their outstanding contributions to the construction industry. The editors' comment:

"Their efforts, singularly and collectively, helped shape this nation and the world. Each pioneered in often uncharted territory, developing new analytical tools, equipment, engineering or architectural designs. Through their companies, they also invented new means and methods for constructing the built environment."

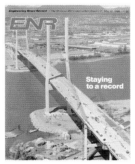

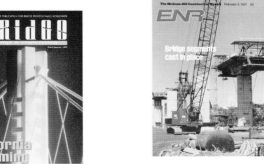
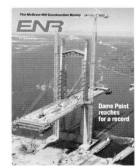

Bridge on the Covers !

Many bridges contained in this book were on the cover of various magazines. Here are some of them.

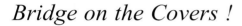

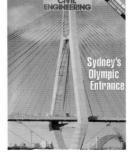
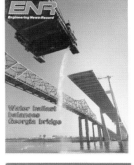

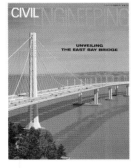
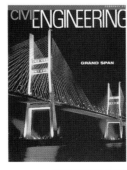
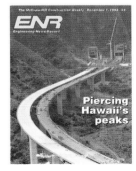

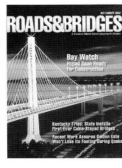

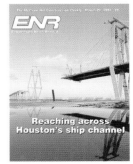

Let Us Build Bridges

Bridges connect communities; bridges connect people. They bring us closer together so we can touch each other!

I hope that by presenting these beautiful, very visible bridges to you, I may also challenge you to join me to build the equally important, but invisible bridges - the bridges of understanding, the bridges of friendship, the bridges of love, between people, between nations, between races and between religions, so that peace will be upon us, and ever after!

Man-Chung Tang

Man-Chung Tang, *Dr.-Ing, Dr.-Ing. e.h., D.Litt., PE*

Dr. Man-Chung Tang is a structural engineer. His work includes bridges, buildings and various types of structures.

His work on bridges encompasses all aspects of design and construction - from conceptualization to final execution, and in many cases also the design of construction equipment. This includes over a hundred bridges, six of them world-record spans at time of completion.

His work can be found in many countries around the world - "the sun never sets on his bridges!"

He is a member of the US National Academy of Engineering, a foreign member of the Chinese Academy of Engineering, an honorary member of the American Society of Civil Engineers and an honorary professor of Tsinghua, Southeast and several other universities in China.

He received his B.Sc. degree in Civil Engineering from Chu Hai College, Hong Kong in 1959, his Diploma of Engineering from Technical University of Darmstadt, Germany, in 1963, majoring in Steel Structures with a minor in Cranes and Conveyor Technology, and his Doctor of Engineering in 1965, also from Technical University of Darmstadt.

He joined the steel conglomerate Gutehoffnungshuette, Oberhausen, Germany in 1965, Severud & Associates, New York in 1968, Dyckerhoff & Widmann, New York in 1970 and established the consulting engineering firms DRC Consultants, Inc. in 1978 and Contech Consultants, Inc in 1983. In 1995, his firms merged with T.Y. Lin International of San Francisco, where he serves as the Chairman of the Board and Technical Director.

From 1989 to 1995, he was an adjunct professor at Columbia University, New York. He has been active in many technical committees and has published over 100 technical papers.

He loves bridges, and his wife, Yee-Yun, loves what he does.

[Dr.-Ing. is Doctor of Engineering, Dr.-Ing. e.h. is Honorary Doctor of Engineering in German]

A Link in the Sky !
ALRT Skytrain, Vancouver, Canada

Dames Point Bridge, Jacksonville, Florida